HAMLET
An Actor Prepares

by
HARRY VENNING

Foreword by
Kenneth Branagh

VIRGIN

First Published in Great Britain in 1990 by
Virgin Books
A division of W.H. Allen & Co Plc
338 Ladbroke Grove
London W10 5AH

ISBN 0 86369 382 2

Designed by Paperweight
Set in Korinna by V.I.P. Type Ltd
Printed and bound in Great Britain

For Lisa, my Faddy

Acknowledgements

I should like to thank (gush!) *The Stage and Television Today*, Jeremy Jehu, Lisa Taylor, Jill Brookbank and Debra Ziegler for their help and support (blub!). Special thanks (weep) to John Davitt (*Spotlight* no. 1228) for all the hours he has sacrificed in helping me research sitting around in pubs (blub, weep, sob, gush, gush, etc.).

Foreword

In Stanislavski's little-known work, *Building a Caricature*, the great master of theatre remarks, 'Say what you like, love, but there aren't many laughs in *Hamlet*.'

Well, yes - and no.

Shakespeare's prince may be a bit short on the funnies - plenty of irony and deadly wit, granted, but a low gag count.

Not so Hamlet the pig.

This porky hero is a comic artist whom the Wittenberg wonder and I could both applaud. Though often cast down and 'chop fall'n', this game and gammon performer continues to show us the gristly truth of an actor's life as he valiantly fails to bring home the bacon.

True ham this Hamlet may be, but I recognise a streaky genius that would shine in any company. Sadly, though, not mine - I'm prepared to offer him fame, fortune, stardom, his choice of leading lady and his name in lights, but he never returns my calls. Too busy in the pub - or perhaps he just draws the line at working with humans.

I hope you will enjoy these cartoons as much as I do. Fluellen in Shakespeare's *Henry V* best expresses my respectful admiration when he says, 'I pray you, is not "pig" great?'

And the greatest pig of all is Hamlet - a true actor for our time.

3

HAMLET

Unquestionably the Brando of his generation. Both are very fat and neither has worked in years.

BRUTUS

Gritty, no-nonsense Northern actor once described as 'Albert Finney with feathers' after his acclaimed performance in *Look Quack in Anger*. Early promise has yet to be fulfilled.

OPHELIA

Born into a showbiz family (mother 'Best of Breed', Crufts '79), Ophelia's love of theatre is second only to Ophelia's love of Ophelia.

ACCRINGTON STANLEY FOOTBALL CLUB.
Defunct 1963.

GRANVILLE
An actor whose presence, charisma, personality, charm and wit has earned him a great deal of work in crowd scenes.

YOUNG VIC
Hamlet's nephew and a student of drama, seen here reading Professor Henrik Oslogrieg's standard textbook, *Performing Strindberg Without Giggling.*

THE ACTING GAME

YOU WILL NEED....

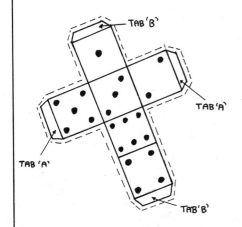

A. DICE....

EQUITY CARD

THIS CARD ENTITLES
THE BEARER TO LORD
IT OVER ACTORS WITHOUT
ONE BUT REALLY NOT
MUCH ELSE.

.... AN EQUITY CARD...

STINKS!
RUBBISH RHINO!
DREADFUL RHINO IN AWFUL PLAY
RHINO IN A STINKER

.... A THICK SKIN

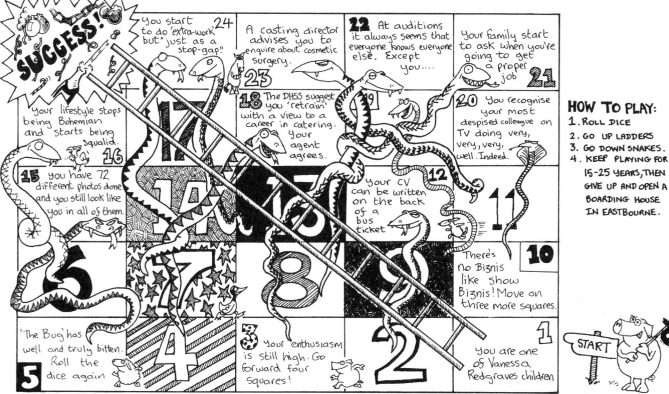

SUCCESS!

24 You start to do 'extra-work' but "just as a stop-gap!"

23 A casting director advises you to enquire about cosmetic surgery.

22 At auditions it always seems that everyone knows everyone else. Except you....

21 Your family start to ask when you're going to get a proper job

16 Your lifestyle stops being Bohemian and starts being squalid.

18 The DHSS suggest you 'retrain' with a view to a career in catering. Your agent agrees.

19

20 You recognise your most despised colleague on TV doing very, very, very, well. Indeed.

15 You have 72 different photos done and you still look like you in all of them.

17

14

13

12 Your CV can be written on the back of a bus ticket

11

6

7

8

9

10 There's no Biznis like show Biznis! Move on three more squares.

5 'The Bug' has well and truly bitten. Roll the dice again

4

3 Your enthusiasm is still high. Go forward four squares!

2

1 You are one of Vanessa Redgraves children

START

HOW TO PLAY:
1. ROLL DICE
2. GO UP LADDERS
3. GO DOWN SNAKES.
4. KEEP PLAYING FOR 15-25 YEARS, THEN GIVE UP AND OPEN A BOARDING HOUSE IN EASTBOURNE.

See you later, Uncle Hamlet, I've got to get to Drama College.

Drama college indeed! Take it from me, my lad, you can't just go to school and learn how to be an actor.

Maybe not, Uncle Hamlet, but I can't stop and chat or I'll be late for my lecture on "Getting your way in Rehearsals by throwing tantrums and sulking"

Then again...

9

13

17

This year is the 125th Anniversary of the birth of Constantin Stanislavski, inventor of the famous "method" school of acting.

In honour of this occasion I am helping Hamlet create a cake

So, what kind of cake are you?

I'm an angry cake, Nobody likes my marzipan.

Good, good!

My currants! My currants need motivation!

Find it, find it!....

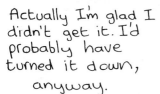

28

35

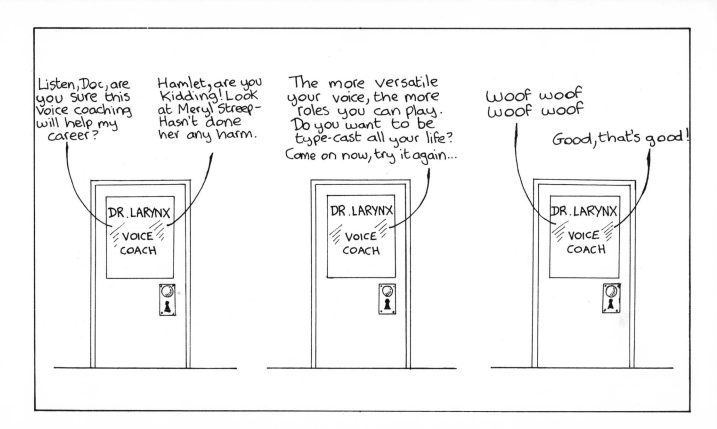

47

50

HAMLET.... **HAMLET!**... HAM-LET!
Spelt? How do you think it's spelt?
H for Hippodrome, A for Alhambra...
Hamlet! Come on now, surely
you must remember me

Look like? You know what
I look like!! Medium height,
squat, snouty nose, curly
tail. Oh, for Pete's sake!
You can't have forgotten me.

I'm sorry, I seem to have lost all records of your existence

I wouldn't mind,
but this is my agent.

61

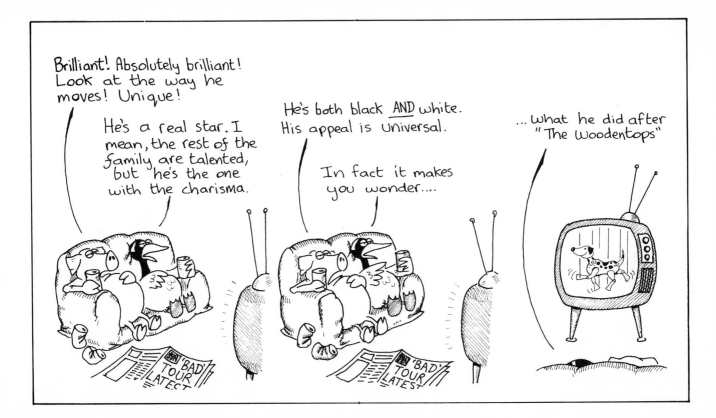

68

70

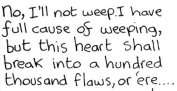

No, I'll not weep. I have full cause of weeping, but this heart shall break into a hundred thousand flaws, or 'ere....

Thank you, NEXT!

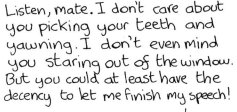

Listen, mate. I don't care about you picking your teeth and yawning. I don't even mind you staring out of the window. But you could at least have the decency to let me finish my speech!

Thank you, **NEXT!**

Er, when I asked you to help me practise for auditions this isn't quite what I meant.

Just trying to keep things authentic.

Dear Dustin,

    I hope you don't mind me calling you Dustin. I take the liberty as we are both brothers in that great family, Showbiz.

    I'm just writing to say how excited we all are that you have decided to grace our humble British boards as Shylock in 'The Merchant of Venice'. Being a thesp myself I know just how thoroughly you Method johnnies like to research a role, and if it would in any way assist you find motivation for your character I should be only too happy to help you by borrowing, say, ₤500.......

Dear Andrew,

Hope you don't mind me calling you Andrew. I take the liberty as we are both brothers in that great family called 'Showbiz'.

The reason I'm writing is to clear up an unfortunate misunderstanding. You see, back in 1973 I wrote a musical called 'You Get Nowt For Coming Second' based on the life of Billy Bremner (Leeds Utd & Scotland). Imagine my surprise when several of the tunes appeared on your recent compilation album 'Premiere Collection'. Now it may well be a complete coincidence, but even the deafest of High Court Judges could spot the similarities between 'Tell Me On A Sunday' and my own 'It's a game of 90 minutes', whilst 'Pie Jesu' is a dead ringer for 'Norman Hunter's Early Bath'. Need I go on?

As it happens I desperately need £25,000 for tap dancing lessons and was wondering if......